W9-CZF-800

Classics for Beginning Readers™

Reader's Digest Young Families

The Adventures of Robin Hood

Designers: Wendy Boccuzzi and Elaine Lopez
Editor: Sharon Yates
Editorial Director: Pamela Pia

Adapted text by Tom DeFalco copyright © 2003 Reader's Digest Young Families, Inc.
Based on the original stories written by Howard Pyle.
Illustrations by Frank Mayo copyright © 2003 Reader's Digest Young Families, Inc.

All rights reserved. No part of this publication may be reproduced or utilized
in any form or by any means, electronic or mechanical, including photocopying,
recording or by any information storage or retrieval system, without
written permission from the publisher.

The Classics for Beginning Readers logo and Reader's Digest Young Families
are registered trademarks of The Reader's Digest Association, Inc.

Printed in China.

Reader's Digest Young Families

The Adventures of Robin Hood

Based on the stories written in 1883
by
Howard Pyle

Retold by Tom DeFalco

Illustrations by
Frank Mayo

$\mathcal{L}$ong ago in England, King Richard was forced to give up his throne. The greedy and unfair Sheriff of Nottingham used this as an opportunity to take advantage of the poor people of his town.

A young archer named Robin Hood and his band of Merry Men remained loyal to King Richard. They vowed to protect the people of Nottingham from the sheriff. The sheriff considered Robin and his men outlaws.

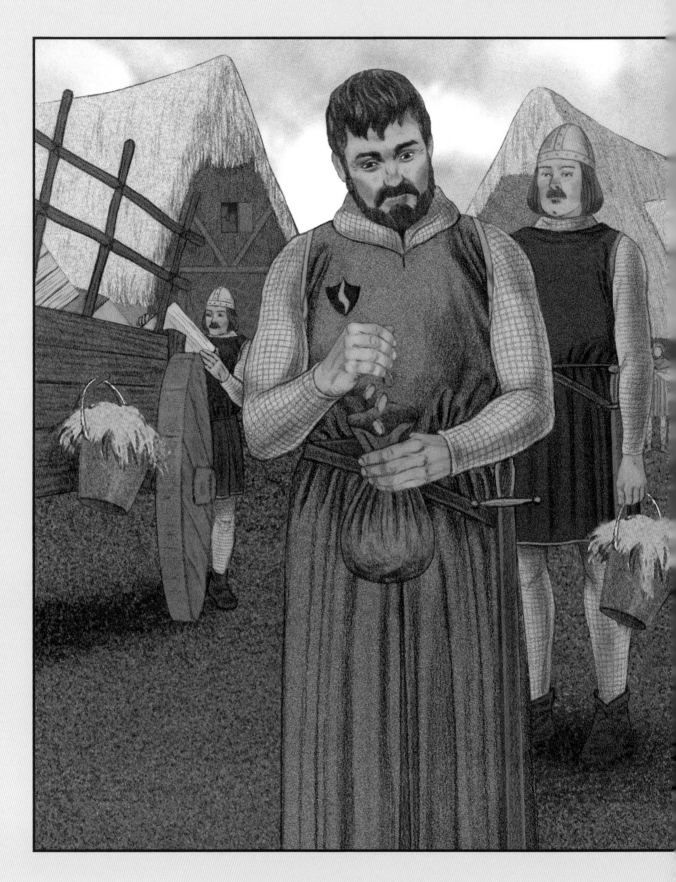

The Sheriff of Nottingham and his men collected as much money as they could from the poor people of Nottingham. If the villagers did not cooperate, they were arrested and put in jail. Sometimes the sheriff's men would burn down villagers' homes. This had happened to Robin Hood himself which was why he lived in Sherwood Forest.

Over time, the sheriff got richer and richer and the people of Nottingham became poorer and poorer.

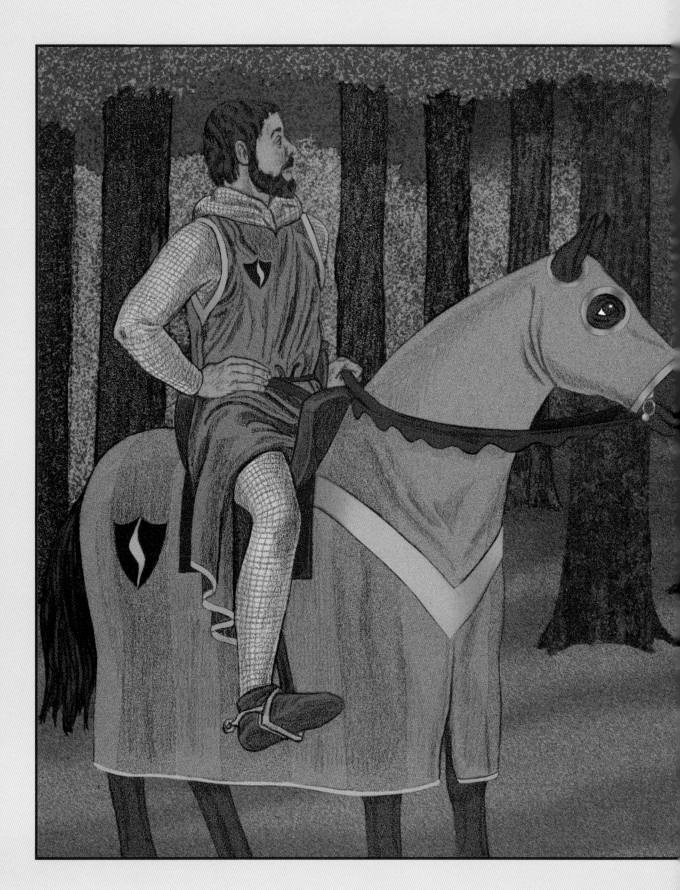

Often Robin and his band stopped the sheriff's men when they rode through Sherwood Forest. Robin would take back the people's money while making the men return to town in their underwear. The men were embarrassed and the sheriff was angry.

The sheriff had tried to capture Robin and the Merry Men many times, but he failed again and again. This also made him angry.

To carry out his good deeds, Robin needed more money than he was able to take from the sheriff's men. Often, he stopped wealthy travelers who passed through Sherwood Forest. Robin would politely ask each one, "Would you like to make a donation to the poor?" If the traveler said "yes," Robin would take only half his money. If he said "no," Robin took it all.

With the money he collected, Robin bought
food, clothes and other necessities for the poor
folk of Nottingham. If there was any money
left over, Robin used it to pay for things needed in
his future raids against the sheriff and his men.

One sunny morning, Robin Hood was out walking in Sherwood Forest. He came to a stream that had a very narrow log across it as a bridge. Robin stepped on to the log just as the biggest man he had ever seen stepped on to the other end. The two men met in the middle.

The big man yelled at Robin, "Get out of my way or you will take an unexpected bath."

"You should be a gentleman and let me go first," Robin replied.

"I am no gentleman," the big man said, and he tried to push Robin into the water.

Since the log was quite slippery, both men lost their balance and fell into the stream. Neither man was hurt, and they eyed each other angrily. But they looked so ridiculous completely soaked, they suddenly burst out laughing.

"You are a good sport," Robin said. "Would you like to join my band of Merry Men? Tell me your name."

"I am Little John," the man said. "And you must be Robin Hood. I've heard a lot about you. Yes, I'd be honored to join your group."

Robin took Little John back to camp and introduced him to the other Merry Men. There was Friar Tuck, who liked to eat. There was Will Scarlet, who was Robin's cousin and always wore a big red rose. There was Alan-A-Dale, a traveling singer, and Much the Miller's son.

Robin Hood was in love with a beautiful Nottingham lady named Maid Marian. He first spotted her in the crowd, while she was watching an archery contest. Marian was so impressed with Robin's skill and charm that she secretly joined forces with him. Maid Marian was also angered by the sheriff's treatment of Nottingham's poor people and decided to help Robin and his men whenever she could.

One day Maid Marian wanted to visit Robin Hood in Sherwood Forest, but she was afraid someone might follow her. So she disguised herself as a young nobleman.

Of course Robin Hood did not recognize Marian so he stopped her as he did other wealthy travelers.

"Would you like to make a donation to the poor?" Robin Hood asked politely.

"I don't talk to strangers," Marian growled in a disguised voice, seeing if she could fool him some more. "My sword shall speak for me!"

Maid Marian jumped down from her horse. As Robin rushed toward her, he tripped on a tree root and fell to the ground.

"I seem to be at your mercy," Robin said with a nervous smile.

"And you always will be!" Marian laughed as she took off her hat revealing her true identity to him.

That evening, Marian joined Robin and the Merry Men for dinner around a campfire. Afterwards they made sure she reached home safely.

The sheriff had many spies, and after learning about Marian's visit to Robin Hood, he immediately arrested her.

"I can use you to lure Robin Hood from Sherwood Forest and capture him at last," the sheriff said to her with an unpleasant smile.

Early the next morning, the sheriff's men posted signs announcing an archery contest. The winner would wed Maid Marian!

"You cannot go to this contest," Friar Tuck warned Robin. "The sheriff is surely using Marian to set a trap for you."

Robin Hood knew it would be dangerous for him, but he had to rescue Marian!

Robin Hood thought about this situation for a long time before coming up with a plan. On the morning of the contest, he told his men to dress like farmers and peasants. Robin also disguised himself. He used tree sap to darken his hair and placed a patch over one eye. Instead of his usual green clothes, he wore a scarlet robe with a hood over his head.

Over one hundred men had entered the contest. As the target was moved farther and farther away with each round, the number of archers grew smaller.

After a few hours, the only two contestants left were the Sheriff of Nottingham and the stranger in scarlet who was really Robin Hood. The Sheriff shot his last arrow, and it hit the center of the target.

"I am the winner," the Sheriff declared. "No one can beat a perfect bull's-eye!"

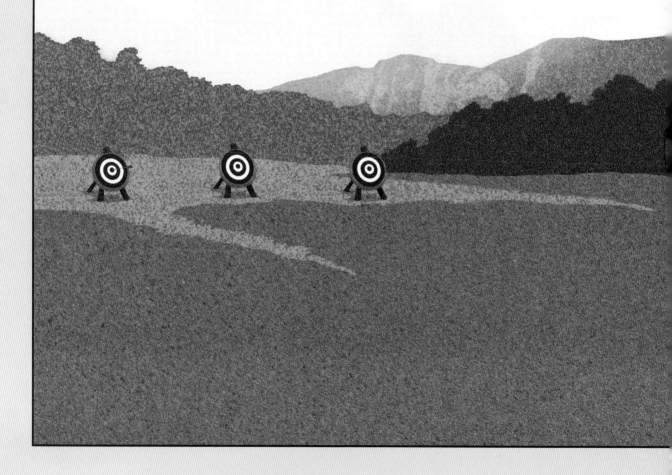

"Not so fast," said the stranger in scarlet as he aimed his bow. "It's my turn." His arrow flew straight at the target and split the sheriff's arrow in half, scoring a second bull's-eye. The crowd gasped!

"Only one man can shoot as well as that," the sheriff said. He ripped off Robin's hood and eye patch. With satisfaction he shouted, "Arrest this man. He is Robin Hood!"

"Not so fast," Robin Hood said again. During the contest, Robin's Merry Men had given weapons to all the villagers. They surrounded the sheriff and his men.

"The people of Nottingham are no longer willing to accept your cruel and heartless actions," Robin Hood said to the sheriff. "Also, we just received news that King Richard has reclaimed his throne. It is you and your men who are under arrest!"

After the sheriff and his men were marched off to the jail, Robin Hood, Maid Marian and the Merry Men returned to Sherwood Forest. There Robin and Marian were married by Friar Tuck, and they lived happily ever after.

In gratitude for Robin's devoted service to the people of Nottingham, the king gave Robin and his men all of Sherwood Forest in which to live in freedom and happiness for the rest of their days.